This *Gratitude* Journal Belongs to:

_____

How to Use this Journal...

Each day, take a few minutes at the start or end of each day, to write down three (3) things that you are grateful for.

This journal has space to write out 52 weeks (an entire year's worth) of gratitude. A quote about gratitude separates each month.

Make it a goal to write in your gratitude journal each day. There is also a space to enter a highlight for each week.

Whenever you are feeling down or anxious, or just want to remind yourself of what you have to be grateful for, review your past entries. Sometimes it's helpful, to be reminded of all the things you are grateful for.

Why not start today by writing out your first entry on the next page.

Happy Journaling!

Today, I'm grateful for: Date: _____

1) _____

2) _____

3) _____

Today, I'm grateful for: Date: _____

1) _____

2) _____

3) _____

Today, I'm grateful for: Date: _____

1) _____

2) _____

3) _____

Today, I'm grateful for: Date: _____

1) _____

2) _____

3) _____

Today, I'm grateful for: Date: _____

1) _____
2) _____
3) _____

Today, I'm grateful for: Date: _____

1) _____
2) _____
3) _____

Today, I'm grateful for: Date: _____

1) _____
2) _____
3) _____

The highlight of my week was...

Today, I'm grateful for: Date: _____

1) _____

2) _____

3) _____

Today, I'm grateful for: Date: _____

1) _____

2) _____

3) _____

Today, I'm grateful for: Date: _____

1) _____

2) _____

3) _____

Today, I'm grateful for: Date: _____

1) _____

2) _____

3) _____

Today, I'm grateful for: Date: _____

1) _____
2) _____
3) _____

Today, I'm grateful for: Date: _____

1) _____
2) _____
3) _____

Today, I'm grateful for: Date: _____

1) _____
2) _____
3) _____

The highlight of my week was...

Today, I'm grateful for: Date: _____

1) _____

2) _____

3) _____

Today, I'm grateful for: Date: _____

1) _____

2) _____

3) _____

Today, I'm grateful for: Date: _____

1) _____

2) _____

3) _____

Today, I'm grateful for: Date: _____

1) _____

2) _____

3) _____

Today, I'm grateful for: Date: _____

1) _____

2) _____

3) _____

Today, I'm grateful for: Date: _____

1) _____

2) _____

3) _____

Today, I'm grateful for: Date: _____

1) _____

2) _____

3) _____

The highlight of my week was...

Today, I'm grateful for: Date: _____

1) _____

2) _____

3) _____

Today, I'm grateful for: Date: _____

1) _____

2) _____

3) _____

Today, I'm grateful for: Date: _____

1) _____

2) _____

3) _____

Today, I'm grateful for: Date: _____

1) _____

2) _____

3) _____

Today, I'm grateful for: Date: _____

1) _____

2) _____

3) _____

Today, I'm grateful for: Date: _____

1) _____

2) _____

3) _____

Today, I'm grateful for: Date: _____

1) _____

2) _____

3) _____

The highlight of my week was...

Gratitude is riches. Complaint is poverty.

-Doris Day

Today, I'm grateful for: Date: _____

1) _____

2) _____

3) _____

Today, I'm grateful for: Date: _____

1) _____

2) _____

3) _____

Today, I'm grateful for: Date: _____

1) _____

2) _____

3) _____

Today, I'm grateful for: Date: _____

1) _____

2) _____

3) _____

Today, I'm grateful for: Date: _____

1) _____

2) _____

3) _____

Today, I'm grateful for: Date: _____

1) _____

2) _____

3) _____

Today, I'm grateful for: Date: _____

1) _____

2) _____

3) _____

The highlight of my week was...

Today, I'm grateful for: Date: _____

1) _____

2) _____

3) _____

Today, I'm grateful for: Date: _____

1) _____

2) _____

3) _____

Today, I'm grateful for: Date: _____

1) _____

2) _____

3) _____

Today, I'm grateful for: Date: _____

1) _____

2) _____

3) _____

Today, I'm grateful for: Date: _____

1) _____

2) _____

3) _____

Today, I'm grateful for: Date: _____

1) _____

2) _____

3) _____

Today, I'm grateful for: Date: _____

1) _____

2) _____

3) _____

The highlight of my week was...

Today, I'm grateful for: Date: _____

1) _____

2) _____

3) _____

Today, I'm grateful for: Date: _____

1) _____

2) _____

3) _____

Today, I'm grateful for: Date: _____

1) _____

2) _____

3) _____

Today, I'm grateful for: Date: _____

1) _____

2) _____

3) _____

Today, I'm grateful for: Date: _____

1) _____

2) _____

3) _____

Today, I'm grateful for: Date: _____

1) _____

2) _____

3) _____

Today, I'm grateful for: Date: _____

1) _____

2) _____

3) _____

The highlight of my week was...

Today, I'm grateful for: Date: _____

1) _____

2) _____

3) _____

Today, I'm grateful for: Date: _____

1) _____

2) _____

3) _____

Today, I'm grateful for: Date: _____

1) _____

2) _____

3) _____

Today, I'm grateful for: Date: _____

1) _____

2) _____

3) _____

Today, I'm grateful for:

Date: _____

1) _____

2) _____

3) _____

Today, I'm grateful for:

Date: _____

1) _____

2) _____

3) _____

Today, I'm grateful for:

Date: _____

1) _____

2) _____

3) _____

The highlight of my week was...

Gratitude and attitude are not challenges; they are choices.

-Robert Braathe

Today, I'm grateful for: Date: _____

1) _____

2) _____

3) _____

Today, I'm grateful for: Date: _____

1) _____

2) _____

3) _____

Today, I'm grateful for: Date: _____

1) _____

2) _____

3) _____

Today, I'm grateful for: Date: _____

1) _____

2) _____

3) _____

Today, I'm grateful for: Date: _____

1) _____

2) _____

3) _____

Today, I'm grateful for: Date: _____

1) _____

2) _____

3) _____

Today, I'm grateful for: Date: _____

1) _____

2) _____

3) _____

The highlight of my week was...

Today, I'm grateful for: Date: _____

1) _____
2) _____
3) _____

Today, I'm grateful for: Date: _____

1) _____
2) _____
3) _____

Today, I'm grateful for: Date: _____

1) _____
2) _____
3) _____

Today, I'm grateful for: Date: _____

1) _____
2) _____
3) _____

Today, I'm grateful for: Date: _____

1) _____

2) _____

3) _____

Today, I'm grateful for: Date: _____

1) _____

2) _____

3) _____

Today, I'm grateful for: Date: _____

1) _____

2) _____

3) _____

The highlight of my week was...

Today, I'm grateful for: Date: _____

1) _____

2) _____

3) _____

Today, I'm grateful for: Date: _____

1) _____

2) _____

3) _____

Today, I'm grateful for: Date: _____

1) _____

2) _____

3) _____

Today, I'm grateful for: Date: _____

1) _____

2) _____

3) _____

Today, I'm grateful for: Date: _____

1) _____
2) _____
3) _____

Today, I'm grateful for: Date: _____

1) _____
2) _____
3) _____

Today, I'm grateful for: Date: _____

1) _____
2) _____
3) _____

The highlight of my week was...

Today, I'm grateful for: Date: _____

1) _____
2) _____
3) _____

Today, I'm grateful for: Date: _____

1) _____
2) _____
3) _____

Today, I'm grateful for: Date: _____

1) _____
2) _____
3) _____

Today, I'm grateful for: Date: _____

1) _____
2) _____
3) _____

Today, I'm grateful for: Date: _____

1) _____
2) _____
3) _____

Today, I'm grateful for: Date: _____

1) _____
2) _____
3) _____

Today, I'm grateful for: Date: _____

1) _____
2) _____
3) _____

The highlight of my week was...

When you are
grateful, fear
disappears and
abundance appears.

-Anthony Robbins

Today, I'm grateful for: Date: _____

1) _____
2) _____
3) _____

Today, I'm grateful for: Date: _____

1) _____
2) _____
3) _____

Today, I'm grateful for: Date: _____

1) _____
2) _____
3) _____

Today, I'm grateful for: Date: _____

1) _____
2) _____
3) _____

Today, I'm grateful for: Date: _____

1) _____

2) _____

3) _____

Today, I'm grateful for: Date: _____

1) _____

2) _____

3) _____

Today, I'm grateful for: Date: _____

1) _____

2) _____

3) _____

The highlight of my week was...

Today, I'm grateful for: Date: _____

1) _____

2) _____

3) _____

Today, I'm grateful for: Date: _____

1) _____

2) _____

3) _____

Today, I'm grateful for: Date: _____

1) _____

2) _____

3) _____

Today, I'm grateful for: Date: _____

1) _____

2) _____

3) _____

Today, I'm grateful for: Date: _____

1) _____

2) _____

3) _____

Today, I'm grateful for: Date: _____

1) _____

2) _____

3) _____

Today, I'm grateful for: Date: _____

1) _____

2) _____

3) _____

The highlight of my week was...

Today, I'm grateful for: Date: _____

1) _____
2) _____
3) _____

Today, I'm grateful for: Date: _____

1) _____
2) _____
3) _____

Today, I'm grateful for: Date: _____

1) _____
2) _____
3) _____

Today, I'm grateful for: Date: _____

1) _____
2) _____
3) _____

Today, I'm grateful for: Date: _____

1) _____
2) _____
3) _____

Today, I'm grateful for: Date: _____

1) _____
2) _____
3) _____

Today, I'm grateful for: Date: _____

1) _____
2) _____
3) _____

The highlight of my week was...

Today, I'm grateful for: Date: _____

1) _____

2) _____

3) _____

Today, I'm grateful for: Date: _____

1) _____

2) _____

3) _____

Today, I'm grateful for: Date: _____

1) _____

2) _____

3) _____

Today, I'm grateful for: Date: _____

1) _____

2) _____

3) _____

Today, I'm grateful for: Date: _____

1) _____

2) _____

3) _____

Today, I'm grateful for: Date: _____

1) _____

2) _____

3) _____

Today, I'm grateful for: Date: _____

1) _____

2) _____

3) _____

The highlight of my week was...

We often take for granted the very things that most deserve our gratitude.

-Cynthia Ozick

Today, I'm grateful for: Date: _____

1) _____

2) _____

3) _____

Today, I'm grateful for: Date: _____

1) _____

2) _____

3) _____

Today, I'm grateful for: Date: _____

1) _____

2) _____

3) _____

Today, I'm grateful for: Date: _____

1) _____

2) _____

3) _____

Today, I'm grateful for: Date: _____

1) _____

2) _____

3) _____

Today, I'm grateful for: Date: _____

1) _____

2) _____

3) _____

Today, I'm grateful for: Date: _____

1) _____

2) _____

3) _____

The highlight of my week was...

Today, I'm grateful for: Date: _____

1) _____

2) _____

3) _____

Today, I'm grateful for: Date: _____

1) _____

2) _____

3) _____

Today, I'm grateful for: Date: _____

1) _____

2) _____

3) _____

Today, I'm grateful for: Date: _____

1) _____

2) _____

3) _____

Today, I'm grateful for: Date: _____

1) _____

2) _____

3) _____

Today, I'm grateful for: Date: _____

1) _____

2) _____

3) _____

Today, I'm grateful for: Date: _____

1) _____

2) _____

3) _____

The highlight of my week was...

Today, I'm grateful for: Date: _____

1) _____

2) _____

3) _____

Today, I'm grateful for: Date: _____

1) _____

2) _____

3) _____

Today, I'm grateful for: Date: _____

1) _____

2) _____

3) _____

Today, I'm grateful for: Date: _____

1) _____

2) _____

3) _____

Today, I'm grateful for: Date: _____

1) _____
2) _____
3) _____

Today, I'm grateful for: Date: _____

1) _____
2) _____
3) _____

Today, I'm grateful for: Date: _____

1) _____
2) _____
3) _____

The highlight of my week was...

Today, I'm grateful for: Date: _____

1) _____
2) _____
3) _____

Today, I'm grateful for: Date: _____

1) _____
2) _____
3) _____

Today, I'm grateful for: Date: _____

1) _____
2) _____
3) _____

Today, I'm grateful for: Date: _____

1) _____
2) _____
3) _____

Today, I'm grateful for: Date: _____

1) _____

2) _____

3) _____

Today, I'm grateful for: Date: _____

1) _____

2) _____

3) _____

Today, I'm grateful for: Date: _____

1) _____

2) _____

3) _____

The highlight of my week was...

Joy is the simplest form of gratitude.

-Karl Barth

Today, I'm grateful for: Date: _____

1) _____

2) _____

3) _____

Today, I'm grateful for: Date: _____

1) _____

2) _____

3) _____

Today, I'm grateful for: Date: _____

1) _____

2) _____

3) _____

Today, I'm grateful for: Date: _____

1) _____

2) _____

3) _____

Today, I'm grateful for: Date: _____

1) _____

2) _____

3) _____

Today, I'm grateful for: Date: _____

1) _____

2) _____

3) _____

Today, I'm grateful for: Date: _____

1) _____

2) _____

3) _____

The highlight of my week was...

Today, I'm grateful for: Date: _____

1) _____
2) _____
3) _____

Today, I'm grateful for: Date: _____

1) _____
2) _____
3) _____

Today, I'm grateful for: Date: _____

1) _____
2) _____
3) _____

Today, I'm grateful for: Date: _____

1) _____
2) _____
3) _____

Today, I'm grateful for: Date: _____

1) _____
2) _____
3) _____

Today, I'm grateful for: Date: _____

1) _____
2) _____
3) _____

Today, I'm grateful for: Date: _____

1) _____
2) _____
3) _____

The highlight of my week was...

Today, I'm grateful for: Date: _____

1) _____
2) _____
3) _____

Today, I'm grateful for: Date: _____

1) _____
2) _____
3) _____

Today, I'm grateful for: Date: _____

1) _____
2) _____
3) _____

Today, I'm grateful for: Date: _____

1) _____
2) _____
3) _____

Today, I'm grateful for: Date: _____

1) _____

2) _____

3) _____

Today, I'm grateful for: Date: _____

1) _____

2) _____

3) _____

Today, I'm grateful for: Date: _____

1) _____

2) _____

3) _____

The highlight of my week was...

Today, I'm grateful for:　　　　Date: _____

1) _____
2) _____
3) _____

Today, I'm grateful for:　　　　Date: _____

1) _____
2) _____
3) _____

Today, I'm grateful for:　　　　Date: _____

1) _____
2) _____
3) _____

Today, I'm grateful for:　　　　Date: _____

1) _____
2) _____
3) _____

Today, I'm grateful for: Date: _____

1) _____
2) _____
3) _____

Today, I'm grateful for: Date: _____

1) _____
2) _____
3) _____

Today, I'm grateful for: Date: _____

1) _____
2) _____
3) _____

The highlight of my week was...

What separates
privilege from
entitlement is
gratitude.

-Brene Brown

Today, I'm grateful for: Date: _____

1) _____

2) _____

3) _____

Today, I'm grateful for: Date: _____

1) _____

2) _____

3) _____

Today, I'm grateful for: Date: _____

1) _____

2) _____

3) _____

Today, I'm grateful for: Date: _____

1) _____

2) _____

3) _____

Today, I'm grateful for: Date: _____

1) _____

2) _____

3) _____

Today, I'm grateful for: Date: _____

1) _____

2) _____

3) _____

Today, I'm grateful for: Date: _____

1) _____

2) _____

3) _____

The highlight of my week was...

Today, I'm grateful for: Date: _____

1) _____

2) _____

3) _____

Today, I'm grateful for: Date: _____

1) _____

2) _____

3) _____

Today, I'm grateful for: Date: _____

1) _____

2) _____

3) _____

Today, I'm grateful for: Date: _____

1) _____

2) _____

3) _____

Today, I'm grateful for: Date: _____

1) _____

2) _____

3) _____

Today, I'm grateful for: Date: _____

1) _____

2) _____

3) _____

Today, I'm grateful for: Date: _____

1) _____

2) _____

3) _____

The highlight of my week was...

Today, I'm grateful for:

Date: _____

1) _____

2) _____

3) _____

Today, I'm grateful for:

Date: _____

1) _____

2) _____

3) _____

Today, I'm grateful for:

Date: _____

1) _____

2) _____

3) _____

Today, I'm grateful for:

Date: _____

1) _____

2) _____

3) _____

Today, I'm grateful for: Date: _____

1) _____
2) _____
3) _____

Today, I'm grateful for: Date: _____

1) _____
2) _____
3) _____

Today, I'm grateful for: Date: _____

1) _____
2) _____
3) _____

The highlight of my week was...

Today, I'm grateful for: Date: _____

1) _____
2) _____
3) _____

Today, I'm grateful for: Date: _____

1) _____
2) _____
3) _____

Today, I'm grateful for: Date: _____

1) _____
2) _____
3) _____

Today, I'm grateful for: Date: _____

1) _____
2) _____
3) _____

Today, I'm grateful for: Date: _____

1) _____
2) _____
3) _____

Today, I'm grateful for: Date: _____

1) _____
2) _____
3) _____

Today, I'm grateful for: Date: _____

1) _____
2) _____
3) _____

The highlight of my week was...

When we focus on our gratitude, the tide of disappointment goes out and the tide of love rushes in.

-Kristin Armstrong

Today, I'm grateful for: Date: _____

1) _____
2) _____
3) _____

Today, I'm grateful for: Date: _____

1) _____
2) _____
3) _____

Today, I'm grateful for: Date: _____

1) _____
2) _____
3) _____

Today, I'm grateful for: Date: _____

1) _____
2) _____
3) _____

Today, I'm grateful for: Date: _____

1) _____

2) _____

3) _____

Today, I'm grateful for: Date: _____

1) _____

2) _____

3) _____

Today, I'm grateful for: Date: _____

1) _____

2) _____

3) _____

The highlight of my week was...

Today, I'm grateful for: Date: _____

1) _____
2) _____
3) _____

Today, I'm grateful for: Date: _____

1) _____
2) _____
3) _____

Today, I'm grateful for: Date: _____

1) _____
2) _____
3) _____

Today, I'm grateful for: Date: _____

1) _____
2) _____
3) _____

Today, I'm grateful for: Date: _____

1) _____
2) _____
3) _____

Today, I'm grateful for: Date: _____

1) _____
2) _____
3) _____

Today, I'm grateful for: Date: _____

1) _____
2) _____
3) _____

The highlight of my week was...

Today, I'm grateful for: Date: _____

1) _____
2) _____
3) _____

Today, I'm grateful for: Date: _____

1) _____
2) _____
3) _____

Today, I'm grateful for: Date: _____

1) _____
2) _____
3) _____

Today, I'm grateful for: Date: _____

1) _____
2) _____
3) _____

Today, I'm grateful for: Date: _____

1) _____

2) _____

3) _____

Today, I'm grateful for: Date: _____

1) _____

2) _____

3) _____

Today, I'm grateful for: Date: _____

1) _____

2) _____

3) _____

The highlight of my week was...

Today, I'm grateful for: Date: _____

1) _____

2) _____

3) _____

Today, I'm grateful for: Date: _____

1) _____

2) _____

3) _____

Today, I'm grateful for: Date: _____

1) _____

2) _____

3) _____

Today, I'm grateful for: Date: _____

1) _____

2) _____

3) _____

Today, I'm grateful for: Date: _____

1) _____
2) _____
3) _____

Today, I'm grateful for: Date: _____

1) _____
2) _____
3) _____

Today, I'm grateful for: Date: _____

1) _____
2) _____
3) _____

The highlight of my week was...

Those who have the ability to be grateful are the ones who have the ability to achieve greatness.

-Steve Maraboli

Today, I'm grateful for: Date: _____

1) _____

2) _____

3) _____

Today, I'm grateful for: Date: _____

1) _____

2) _____

3) _____

Today, I'm grateful for: Date: _____

1) _____

2) _____

3) _____

Today, I'm grateful for: Date: _____

1) _____

2) _____

3) _____

Today, I'm grateful for: Date: _____

1) _____
2) _____
3) _____

Today, I'm grateful for: Date: _____

1) _____
2) _____
3) _____

Today, I'm grateful for: Date: _____

1) _____
2) _____
3) _____

The highlight of my week was...

Today, I'm grateful for:　　　　　Date: _____

1) _____

2) _____

3) _____

Today, I'm grateful for:　　　　　Date: _____

1) _____

2) _____

3) _____

Today, I'm grateful for:　　　　　Date: _____

1) _____

2) _____

3) _____

Today, I'm grateful for:　　　　　Date: _____

1) _____

2) _____

3) _____

Today, I'm grateful for: Date: _____

1) _____
2) _____
3) _____

Today, I'm grateful for: Date: _____

1) _____
2) _____
3) _____

Today, I'm grateful for: Date: _____

1) _____
2) _____
3) _____

The highlight of my week was...

Today, I'm grateful for: Date: _____

1) _____
2) _____
3) _____

Today, I'm grateful for: Date: _____

1) _____
2) _____
3) _____

Today, I'm grateful for: Date: _____

1) _____
2) _____
3) _____

Today, I'm grateful for: Date: _____

1) _____
2) _____
3) _____

Today, I'm grateful for: Date: _____

1) _____
2) _____
3) _____

Today, I'm grateful for: Date: _____

1) _____
2) _____
3) _____

Today, I'm grateful for: Date: _____

1) _____
2) _____
3) _____

The highlight of my week was...

Today, I'm grateful for: Date: _____

1) _____

2) _____

3) _____

Today, I'm grateful for: Date: _____

1) _____

2) _____

3) _____

Today, I'm grateful for: Date: _____

1) _____

2) _____

3) _____

Today, I'm grateful for: Date: _____

1) _____

2) _____

3) _____

Today, I'm grateful for: Date: _____

1) _____
2) _____
3) _____

Today, I'm grateful for: Date: _____

1) _____
2) _____
3) _____

Today, I'm grateful for: Date: _____

1) _____
2) _____
3) _____

The highlight of my week was...

It's a funny thing about life, once you begin to take note of the things you are grateful for, you begin to lose sight of the things that you lack.

-Germany Kent

Today, I'm grateful for: Date: _____

1) _____

2) _____

3) _____

Today, I'm grateful for: Date: _____

1) _____

2) _____

3) _____

Today, I'm grateful for: Date: _____

1) _____

2) _____

3) _____

Today, I'm grateful for: Date: _____

1) _____

2) _____

3) _____

Today, I'm grateful for: Date: _____

1) _____
2) _____
3) _____

Today, I'm grateful for: Date: _____

1) _____
2) _____
3) _____

Today, I'm grateful for: Date: _____

1) _____
2) _____
3) _____

The highlight of my week was...

Today, I'm grateful for: Date: _____

1) _____
2) _____
3) _____

Today, I'm grateful for: Date: _____

1) _____
2) _____
3) _____

Today, I'm grateful for: Date: _____

1) _____
2) _____
3) _____

Today, I'm grateful for: Date: _____

1) _____
2) _____
3) _____

Today, I'm grateful for: Date: _____

1) _____

2) _____

3) _____

Today, I'm grateful for: Date: _____

1) _____

2) _____

3) _____

Today, I'm grateful for: Date: _____

1) _____

2) _____

3) _____

The highlight of my week was...

Today, I'm grateful for: Date: _____

1) _____
2) _____
3) _____

Today, I'm grateful for: Date: _____

1) _____
2) _____
3) _____

Today, I'm grateful for: Date: _____

1) _____
2) _____
3) _____

Today, I'm grateful for: Date: _____

1) _____
2) _____
3) _____

Today, I'm grateful for: Date: _____

1) _____

2) _____

3) _____

Today, I'm grateful for: Date: _____

1) _____

2) _____

3) _____

Today, I'm grateful for: Date: _____

1) _____

2) _____

3) _____

The highlight of my week was...

Today, I'm grateful for: Date: _____

1) _____
2) _____
3) _____

Today, I'm grateful for: Date: _____

1) _____
2) _____
3) _____

Today, I'm grateful for: Date: _____

1) _____
2) _____
3) _____

Today, I'm grateful for: Date: _____

1) _____
2) _____
3) _____

Today, I'm grateful for: Date: _____

1) _____
2) _____
3) _____

Today, I'm grateful for: Date: _____

1) _____
2) _____
3) _____

Today, I'm grateful for: Date: _____

1) _____
2) _____
3) _____

The highlight of my week was...

There's always something to be grateful for!

Today, I'm grateful for: Date: _____

1) _____
2) _____
3) _____

Today, I'm grateful for: Date: _____

1) _____
2) _____
3) _____

Today, I'm grateful for: Date: _____

1) _____
2) _____
3) _____

Today, I'm grateful for: Date: _____

1) _____
2) _____
3) _____

Today, I'm grateful for: Date: _____

1) _____
2) _____
3) _____

Today, I'm grateful for: Date: _____

1) _____
2) _____
3) _____

Today, I'm grateful for: Date: _____

1) _____
2) _____
3) _____

The highlight of my week was...

Today, I'm grateful for: Date: _____

1) _____

2) _____

3) _____

Today, I'm grateful for: Date: _____

1) _____

2) _____

3) _____

Today, I'm grateful for: Date: _____

1) _____

2) _____

3) _____

Today, I'm grateful for: Date: _____

1) _____

2) _____

3) _____

Today, I'm grateful for: Date: _____

1) _____

2) _____

3) _____

Today, I'm grateful for: Date: _____

1) _____

2) _____

3) _____

Today, I'm grateful for: Date: _____

1) _____

2) _____

3) _____

The highlight of my week was...

Today, I'm grateful for: Date: _____

1) _____

2) _____

3) _____

Today, I'm grateful for: Date: _____

1) _____

2) _____

3) _____

Today, I'm grateful for: Date: _____

1) _____

2) _____

3) _____

Today, I'm grateful for: Date: _____

1) _____

2) _____

3) _____

Today, I'm grateful for: Date: _____

1) _____

2) _____

3) _____

Today, I'm grateful for: Date: _____

1) _____

2) _____

3) _____

Today, I'm grateful for: Date: _____

1) _____

2) _____

3) _____

The highlight of my week was...

Today, I'm grateful for: Date: _____

1) _____

2) _____

3) _____

Today, I'm grateful for: Date: _____

1) _____

2) _____

3) _____

Today, I'm grateful for: Date: _____

1) _____

2) _____

3) _____

Today, I'm grateful for: Date: _____

1) _____

2) _____

3) _____

Today, I'm grateful for: Date: _____

1) _____

2) _____

3) _____

Today, I'm grateful for: Date: _____

1) _____

2) _____

3) _____

Today, I'm grateful for: Date: _____

1) _____

2) _____

3) _____

The highlight of my week was...

Those with a grateful mindset tend to see the message in the mess. And even though life may knock them down, the grateful find reasons, if even small ones, to get up.

-Steve Maraboli

Today, I'm grateful for:

Date: _____

1) _____
2) _____
3) _____

Today, I'm grateful for:

Date: _____

1) _____
2) _____
3) _____

Today, I'm grateful for:

Date: _____

1) _____
2) _____
3) _____

Today, I'm grateful for:

Date: _____

1) _____
2) _____
3) _____

Today, I'm grateful for: Date: _____

1) _____
2) _____
3) _____

Today, I'm grateful for: Date: _____

1) _____
2) _____
3) _____

Today, I'm grateful for: Date: _____

1) _____
2) _____
3) _____

The highlight of my week was...

Today, I'm grateful for: Date: _____

1) _____
2) _____
3) _____

Today, I'm grateful for: Date: _____

1) _____
2) _____
3) _____

Today, I'm grateful for: Date: _____

1) _____
2) _____
3) _____

Today, I'm grateful for: Date: _____

1) _____
2) _____
3) _____

Today, I'm grateful for: Date: _____

1) _____
2) _____
3) _____

Today, I'm grateful for: Date: _____

1) _____
2) _____
3) _____

Today, I'm grateful for: Date: _____

1) _____
2) _____
3) _____

The highlight of my week was...

Today, I'm grateful for: Date: _____

1) _____

2) _____

3) _____

Today, I'm grateful for: Date: _____

1) _____

2) _____

3) _____

Today, I'm grateful for: Date: _____

1) _____

2) _____

3) _____

Today, I'm grateful for: Date: _____

1) _____

2) _____

3) _____

Today, I'm grateful for: Date: _____

1) _____
2) _____
3) _____

Today, I'm grateful for: Date: _____

1) _____
2) _____
3) _____

Today, I'm grateful for: Date: _____

1) _____
2) _____
3) _____

The highlight of my week was...

Today, I'm grateful for: Date: _____

1) _____
2) _____
3) _____

Today, I'm grateful for: Date: _____

1) _____
2) _____
3) _____

Today, I'm grateful for: Date: _____

1) _____
2) _____
3) _____

Today, I'm grateful for: Date: _____

1) _____
2) _____
3) _____

Today, I'm grateful for:

Date: _____

1) _____

2) _____

3) _____

Today, I'm grateful for:

Date: _____

1) _____

2) _____

3) _____

Today, I'm grateful for:

Date: _____

1) _____

2) _____

3) _____

The highlight of my week was...

Be grateful for what
you already have
while you pursue
your goals. If you
aren't grateful for
what you already
have, what makes
you think you would
be happy with more.

-Roy T. Bennett

Today, I'm grateful for: Date: _____

1) _____
2) _____
3) _____

Today, I'm grateful for: Date: _____

1) _____
2) _____
3) _____

Today, I'm grateful for: Date: _____

1) _____
2) _____
3) _____

Today, I'm grateful for: Date: _____

1) _____
2) _____
3) _____

Today, I'm grateful for: Date: _____

1) _____

2) _____

3) _____

Today, I'm grateful for: Date: _____

1) _____

2) _____

3) _____

Today, I'm grateful for: Date: _____

1) _____

2) _____

3) _____

The highlight of my week was...

Today, I'm grateful for: Date: _____

1) _____

2) _____

3) _____

Today, I'm grateful for: Date: _____

1) _____

2) _____

3) _____

Today, I'm grateful for: Date: _____

1) _____

2) _____

3) _____

Today, I'm grateful for: Date: _____

1) _____

2) _____

3) _____

Today, I'm grateful for: Date: _____

1) _____
2) _____
3) _____

Today, I'm grateful for: Date: _____

1) _____
2) _____
3) _____

Today, I'm grateful for: Date: _____

1) _____
2) _____
3) _____

The highlight of my week was...

Today, I'm grateful for: Date: _____

1) _____
2) _____
3) _____

Today, I'm grateful for: Date: _____

1) _____
2) _____
3) _____

Today, I'm grateful for: Date: _____

1) _____
2) _____
3) _____

Today, I'm grateful for: Date: _____

1) _____
2) _____
3) _____

Today, I'm grateful for: Date: _____

1) _____

2) _____

3) _____

Today, I'm grateful for: Date: _____

1) _____

2) _____

3) _____

Today, I'm grateful for: Date: _____

1) _____

2) _____

3) _____

The highlight of my week was...

Today, I'm grateful for: Date: _____

1) _____

2) _____

3) _____

Today, I'm grateful for: Date: _____

1) _____

2) _____

3) _____

Today, I'm grateful for: Date: _____

1) _____

2) _____

3) _____

Today, I'm grateful for: Date: _____

1) _____

2) _____

3) _____

Today, I'm grateful for: Date: _____

1) _____

2) _____

3) _____

Today, I'm grateful for: Date: _____

1) _____

2) _____

3) _____

Today, I'm grateful for: Date: _____

1) _____

2) _____

3) _____

The highlight of my week was...

Reflections

Reflections

Made in the USA
Middletown, DE
07 March 2023

26379677R00068